Characters

Zhi Li Tang

The youngest daughter of the Emperor, lost during the turbulent end of Northern Song Dynasty. Though formally granted the title of Princess, the Emperor now suspects her parentage.

Zhong Lu Wu

Recalled from many successful campaigns on the battlefield and given the position of Seeker. He hopes to use Zhi Li as a chance to prove his abilities and return to the war, but has fallen in love with her instead.

Yang Liu

Yang Ye's younger sister, kind and gentle, likes Hui Tang.

Hui Tang

He's taken care of Zhi Li since she was a young child. He wants nothing more than to see her title restored. He chose to leave in an attempt to forget his feelings for Zhi Li.

Fang Yao

The Bishop's right-hand man and Zhong Lu's sworn enemy.

Yang Ye

Rebel leader, has ambitions of becoming emperor.

real/fake. Princess

volume 5

Contents

real/fake.
Princess

Chapter 13: Heart's Lonely Sail

I'VE FINALLY ...

FOUND YOU.

FINALLY...

I AM WITH YOU AGAIN...

AH...

YOU CAN'T OPEN THOSE LOCKS...

WITHOUT A KEY.

DON'T WORRY,

I'LL BE RIGHT BACK--

PAH!

YOU MUST LEAVE HERE!

I'LL GO ASK LIU YANG TO HELP.

HOW CAN YOU TREAT ZHI LI THIS WAY?

BROTHER!

YOU, WATCH THOSE TWO!

DON'T LET THEM ESAPE!

LIU...

I JUST ...

GOT MY...

HEART BROKEN.

IT DOESN'T MATTER IF SHE IS THE PRINCESS!

SHE'S AN IMPORTANT PERSON TO DOCTOR TANG!

DON'T WORRY.

I WON'T LET HIM LEAVE THIS PLACE.

BRO-THER!

LIU...

YOU'RE IN LOVE WITH HUI TANG, RIGHT?

BROTHER...

RELEASE THAT MAN LOCKED IN PRISON!

MY WORD IS GOLD!

SO THIS TIME, I WILL LISTEN TO YOU AND LET HIM GO!

HUI...

YOU SAVED ME ONCE ...

BUT I'VE ALREADY BEGUN MY QUEST TO BECOME KING...

SO DON'T TRY TO STOP ME!

I NEED YOUR SUPPORT RIGHT NOW.

STAY AND HELP ME!

I'M JUST A SIMPLE DOCTOR ...

I CAN'T HELP YOU BECOME KING.

WAIT!

IF YOU THINK OF ME AS A TRUE FRIEND, THEN TAKE MY COUNSEL...

PARLAY WITH THE SONG ARMY, DISBAND YOUR CAMP, AND GIVE UP BECOMING KING!

THIS PAST YEAR, I'VE TREATED YOU LIKE A TRUE FRIEND...

WHY WON'T YOU STAY AND HELP ME?

WHY DO YOU ALWAYS STICK UP FOR THE SONG?!

ARE YOU REALLY SO KIND-HEARTED...

OR...

SLAM

I NEED MORE STRENGTH TO PROTECT THIS PLACE!

YOU WILL NEVER UNDERSTAND!

HUI TANG... YOU ONCE SAID...

THAT BECAUSE YOU LEFT HOME AT A YOUNG AGE,

YOU FELT THAT ANYWHERE CAN BECOME HOME, EVERYONE CAN BE A FRIEND.

BUT YOU AND I ARE NOT THE SAME...

THIS IS WHERE I GREW UP.

ZHONG LU! IS YOUR WOUND HURTING AGAIN?

AH...

I'M FINE...

NO MATTER WHAT,

YOU HAVE TO LEAVE THIS PLACE.

CLOP! CLOP! CLOP!

HORSES!?

IT SOUNDS LIKE ONLY ONE PERSON.

I DON'T HAVE ANY WEAPONS ON ME...

BUT THIS IS MORE THAN ENOUGH ...

TO TAKE CARE OF ONE SOLDIER ...

LEAP!

ZHI LI, STAY BEHIND ME!

I CAN'T LET YOU TAKE ZHI LI LIKE THIS!

MASTER WU!

IF SHE GOES BACK TO THE SONG CAMP, SHE'S DEAD.

I KNOW.

I'M NOT PLANNING TO GO BACK THERE.

CLANG!

MASTER WU!

I HAVE BEEN SEARCHING HIGH AND LOW FOR YOU!

real/fake.
Princess

Chapter 14: Before Dawn

SO WHY WOULD HE HELP THESE SOUTHERN REBELS?

HE'S CLEARLY A NORTHER-NER...

BANDITS...

TAKING GOODS FROM THE COMMON FOLKS TO ENRICH THEMSELVES..!.

WHEN THESE OFFICIALS COME COLLECTING TAX MONEY

FROM THE POINT OF VIEW OF THE SOUTHERNERS...

THEY ARE THE REAL BANDITS.

I HAVE TO FIND A WAY TO STOP THE KILLING...

I CAN ONLY HELP PREVENT A FEW DEATHS.

HURRY!

I DON'T WANT HIM TO DIE BEFORE HE CONFESSES!

BRING HIM DOWN!

SIR... SIR!

HE BIT OFF HIS OWN TONGUE!

DAMN!

USE THIS CLOTH TO STUFF HIS MOUTH!

IF I DIE RIGHT NOW...

I DON'T CARE...

STOMP!

YOU!

SLAM!

YOU...

THAT REBEL'S BEEN RESCUED?

YOU CAN'T EVEN TAKE DOWN A BUNCH OF BANDITS!

YOU'RE USELESS!

NOW THE PROBLEM IS...

REALLY... FORGET IT!

THE REBELS CAUSING TROUBLE IS NONE OF MY BUSINESS.

WATCH THE OTHER PRISONER!

MAKE SURE SHE DOESN'T ESCAPE!

WHERE ARE THEY?

THE BANDIT ...

HAS ALREADY BEEN RESCUED BY HIS FELLOW REBELS.

ARE YOU JOKING?

THAT'S NO PRINCESS, THAT'S A CRIMINAL!

THE PRINCESS?

YE YANG ALREADY RESCUED HIM.

YOU HAVE TO HURRY AND LEAVE HERE!

WHERE'S HUI?

THIS IS THE LOCAL CAPITAL,

WHILE WE ARE HERE, FANG YAO WON'T BE ABLE TO COME AFTER US.

YOU CAN REST HERE FOR A WHILE.

I'M TIRED OF RUNNING AWAY.

ZHONG LU...

ZHI LI!

IMPER-SONATING ROYALTY IS A CRIME PUNISHABLE BY DEATH!

ZHI LI?

I DON'T WANT TO HIDE ANYMORE ...

I AM NOT A FAKE PRINCESS YI FU.

I WANT TO SEE MY BROTHER ...

EVEN IF HE WANTS TO KILL ME.

IT NEVER ENDS.

I DON'T WANT TO LIVE LIKE THIS.

WHEN I THINK OF MY MOTHER...

I REMEMBER SOMEONE ELSE BY HER SIDE.

THAT PERSON...

MUST'VE BEEN THE ONE SHE LOVED.

I'M NOT MY MOTHER...

I JUST LOVE HIM...

SO MUCH.

BUT IN THE END...

MOTHER CHOSE FATHER...

SHE CHOSE THE PERSON WHO LOVED HER.

IT'S OKAY IF WE CAN'T BE TOGETHER FOREVER.

I ONLY HOPE THAT HE WILL STAY WITH ME UNTIL DAWN.

THE ONE YOU DRUGGED ME WITH LAST TIME!

THE SLEEPING PILL! I'M TAKING THAT AWAY FROM YOU!

I DON'T WANT YOU TO DO THAT AGAIN!

MEDICINE? WHAT MEDICINE?

GIVE ME THAT MEDICINE!

HUI!

YOU'RE STILL ANGRY ABOUT THAT...

BUT IT'S JUST A PILL...

THAT HELPS YOU SLEEP BETTER AND GIVES YOU GOOD DREAMS.

I HAVE DECIDED...

NOT TO GET ANYONE ELSE INVOLVED.

OR HAVE ANYONE ELSE PROTECT ME.

I WILL BE RESPONSIBLE ... FOR MY OWN AFFAIRS!

PRINCESS ...

YOUR MAJESTY?

WHAT ARE YOU...

DOING HERE?

FANG YAO,

YOU SHOULD FOLLOW IMPERIAL EDICT...

AND TAKE ME BACK FOR SENTENCING!

real/fake.
Princess

Final Chapter: Real Fake Princess

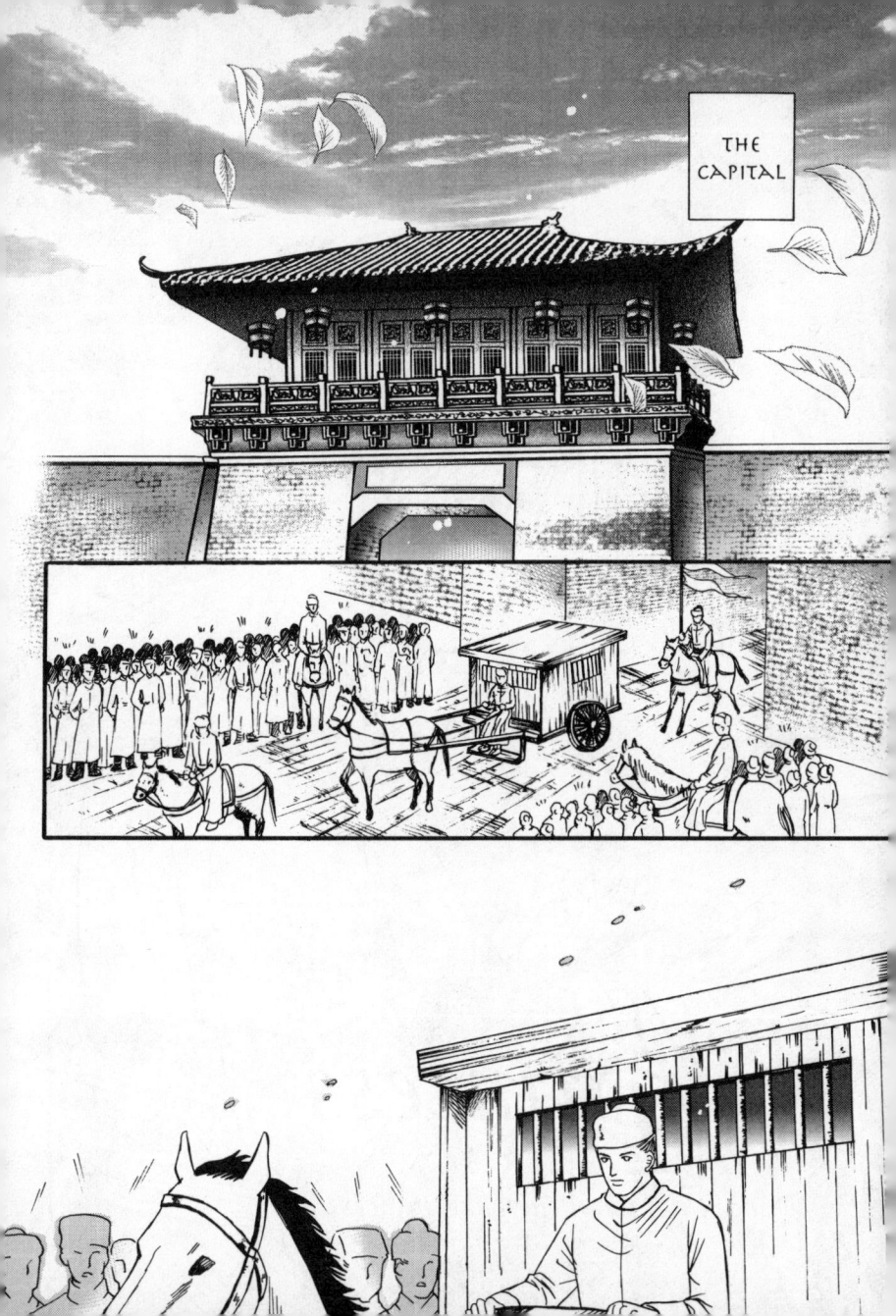

THE CAPITAL

TIME TO EAT.

MISS!

THANK YOU.

THE GUARDS NORMALLY DON'T SPEAK TO ME.

I ORDERED A SPECIAL MEAL FOR YOU.

THE NORMAL GUARD IS SICK, I'M HIS SUB.

THEN WHY DON'T I TALK TO YOU FOR A WHILE?

REALLY?

EAT UP...

YOUR FOOD IS GETTING COLD.

IF THE EMPEROR RECOGNIZED ME...

WOULD HE WANT ME TO CALL HIM "YOUR MAJESTY..."

OR "BROTHER?"

BRO-THER!

THAT'S OKAY...

I THINK...

THE EMPEROR IS NOT WORTHY OF BEING CALLED EITHER!

BECAUSE HE WON'T ACKNOW-LEDGE YOU.

BECAUSE I KNOW...

MY BROTHER WOULD RECOGNIZE ME...

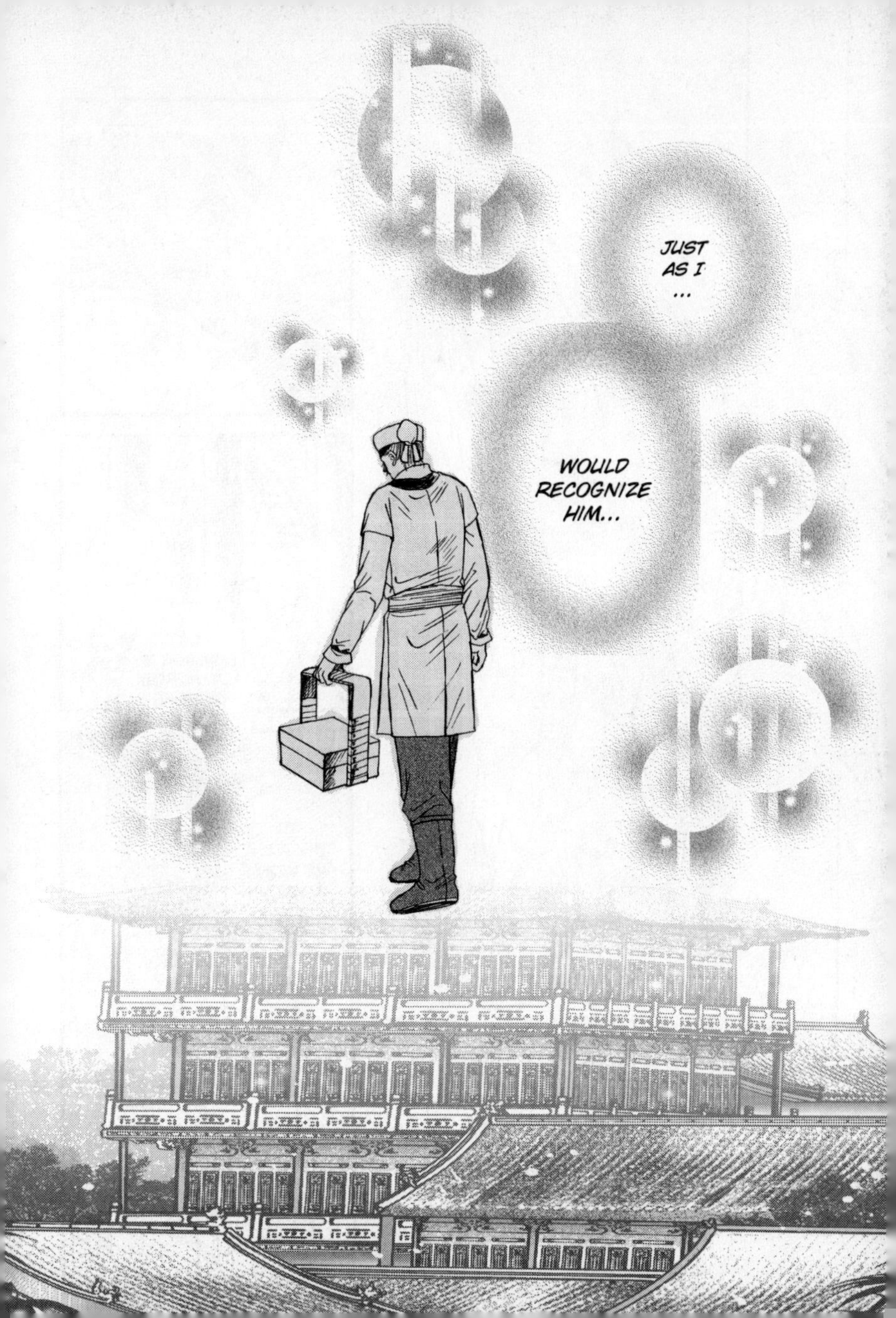
JUST AS I ...
WOULD RECOGNIZE HIM...

ZHONG LU... PRINCESS YI FU IS THE EMPEROR'S SISTER.

THE EMPEROR MUST HAVE A REASON FOR WHAT HE'S DOING!

ARE YOU WILLING TO JUST SIT BY AND WATCH,

AS THEY EXECUTE THE PRINCESS?!

BUT DON'T FORGET ...

PRINCESS YI FU IS THE EMPEROR'S SISTER...

MOTHER ...

ZHONG LU!

I'LL JUST GO RESCUE HER FROM THE PRISON MYSELF!

IT DOESN'T MATTER IF THE EMPEROR WON'T SEE ME!

SHE IS MY WIFE.

MOVE!

SUNLIGHT...

IT'S SO BRIGHT...

I FEEL THAT I NO LONGER...

HAVE ANY REGRETS.

NOW...

MY TIME AS PRINCESS YI FU...

WILL END...

THE ONLY THING I CAN THINK OF IN MY HEART...

I ALWAYS
WANT TO BE BY
YOUR SIDE.

SIR!

SUDDENLY... THERE WAS A STAB OF PAIN IN MY HEART...

I'M FINE!

YOU HAVEN'T SLEPT FOR DAYS AND NOW...

SIR? ARE YOU ALL RIGHT?

HURRY!

Soon... the story of the fake princess,

Spread throughout the land.

During the 12th year, on september 13th...

Her last name was Tang, she was 18 years old.

She was executed.

She pretended to be the younger sister of the emperor, and was punished accordingly...

Year 14

The capital is in a state of peace and harmony.

The song and Jin empires have signed a peace agreement and thus put an end to the war.

The rebel army has been stamped out.

The people enjoy the wise rule of the emperor.

The country begins to prosper.

Music flows, day and night.

THe palace is rebuilt.

YOUR MAJESTY,

MASTER WU IS HERE TO SEE YOU.

ZHONG LU!

YOU'VE FINALLY COME!

SIT, PLEASE!

IMPERIAL FAMILY MEMBERS?

THOUGH THE EMPEROR HAS GRANTED YOU PERMISSION TO QUIT YOUR POST,

THANK YOU, YOUR MAJESTY.

HE HOPES THAT YOU WILL RESUME YOUR DUTIES TO LOOK FOR LOST IMPERIAL FAMILY MEMBERS.

IT'S TOO BAD YOU WILL NO LONGER BE THE SEEKER...

WHEN YOU SEE HER...

DON'T FORGET TO TELL HER THE EMPEROR'S MESSAGE.

THE EMPEROR MAY HAVE KILLED PRINCESS YI FU,

BUT HE STILL LOVES HIS SISTER VERY MUCH.

THIS IS...

FOR YOU FOUND THE PERSON WHO WAS MOST IMPORTANT TO THE EMPEROR...

ZHONG LU...

YES MADAME!

AND DON'T GO OUT FISHING FOR A FEW DAYS.

IT'S JUST A COLD.

DRINK THIS MEDI-CINE AND GET SOME REST.

YE YANG?

LONG TIME NO SEE,

HUI TANG!

I'VE CUT DOWN ...

THE FAKE PRINCESS' HEAD!

GUARDS, SEIZE HIM!

WHAT?

WHO ARE YOU?

YE YANG?

LET'S GO!

WHAT ...

THEN ...

THE SONG ARMY REPELLED OUR ATTACKS... MANY INNOCENTS LOST THEIR LIVES...

I HAD TO PARLAY.

ACTUALLY I CAME HERE...

I'M DOING WELL, BUT SOMEONE ELSE IS NOT DOING SO WELL.

I GUESS I SHOULD THANK YOU!

A KING LIKE ME STILL HAS TO LISTEN TO YOU,

AND GO BE A FARMER!

BECAUSE I HAVE SOMETHING TO ASK OF YOU.

LOOKS LIKE YOU'RE STILL DOING WELL, EVEN IF YOU'RE NOT A KING!

"IF..."

"YOU SURVIVE BY SOME CHANCE ..."

"DON'T EVER COME BACK AGAIN."

"THEN ..."

BUT...

MY HEART FEELS LIKE IT HAS SHRUNK...

TO THE POINT WHERE IT CAN HOLD ONLY ONE PERSON...

SOMEONE I CAN NEVER FORGET...

THE ONE I'VE BEEN DREAMING OF...

I HAVE
FOUND
HER!

HE SHOULD'VE WAITED UNTIL TOMORROW MORNING TO LEAVE...

HE'S SO STUBBORN ...

OH... IT'S GETTING DARK.

I SAW YE YANG EARLIER, AND HE EXPLAINED EVERYTHING TO ME.

ANOTHER STUBBORN IDEA.

REALLY? TOO BAD I JUST GOT...

YOU'RE ONE TO TALK!

YOUR STUBBORN DECISIONS ...

ALMOST GAVE ME A LIFETIME OF PAIN.

TO SHOW
RAYS OF
HOPE.

IS JUST
BEGINNING
...

After the incident, there were still cases of missing family members remaining.

Eventually the Jin sent documents of captured or killed imperial family members,

And things were finally set straight.

As for princess Yi Fu,

No records were found in the Jin, nor in the cities of the Song.

Her where-abouts,

Became an un-solved mystery.

All manners of stories and theories,

Continue to pour forth...

THE END.

AFTER COMPLETING REAL FAKE PRINCESS

Thank you everyone for reading through to the last volume of Real Fake Princess. This work is a sequel of sorts to my first work. It's been about ten years since I originally conceived the idea, and my two works are about 7 or 8 years apart. The link tying the two works together is the character of Hui Tang, whom many readers feel as if they have "watched" grow. It really does seem that way.

For me, it feels like my wish, when I first began researching Song history and designing characters, has finally been completed.

In other words... don't call this work a sequel with an alternate ending, this really, truly is the end of the story. I'm so glad that I was able to write and illustrate the ending that I have always wanted.

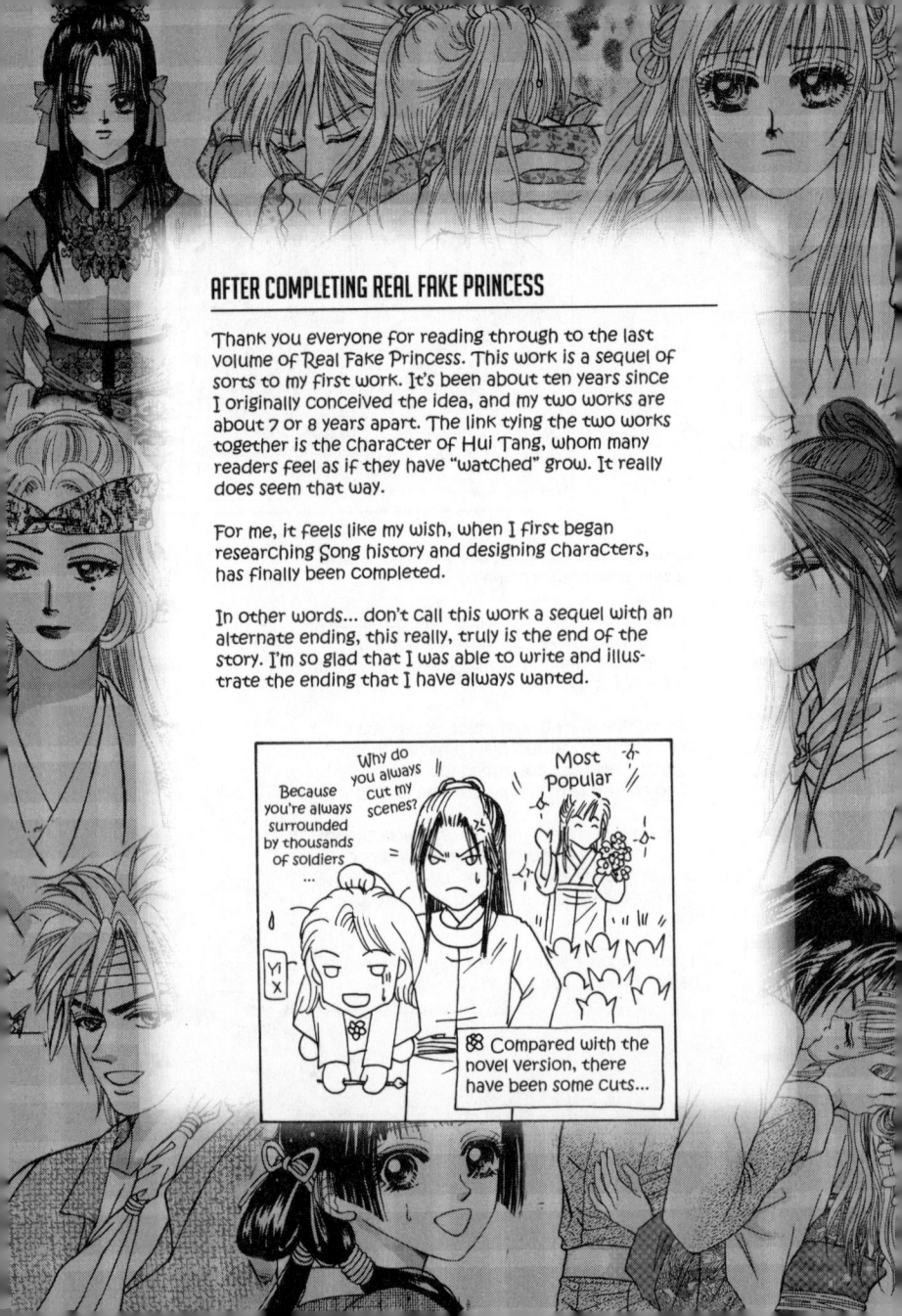

Why do you always cut my scenes?

Because you're always surrounded by thousands of soldiers ...

Most Popular

YI XU

❀ Compared with the novel version, there have been some cuts...

Perhaps... I could have had an ending like this...

Hey!

Baby! Come with me and you'll never have to suffer again!

Boo-hoo...

Yi X

✿ In my original version, Ye Yang was not in love with Zhi Li.

After completing Real Fake Princess, I have to talk about Hui Tang a bit...

According to both polls and readers' letters, Hui's popularity far surpassed Zhong Lu's. However, in the conclusion I didn't have him end up with Zhi Li...

But no one complained much about that, everyone just wanted him to have a "happy" ending... perhaps everyone also wanted Zhi Li to end up with the person she loved most!

In reality, there are many people who cannot be with the one they love, because those people already love someone else. So watch out for those people around you that love you!

Thank you everyone for your support and help, I hope to see you all again soon!

2002.

Loyalty, Betrayal, Romance,

kung-fu.

中華英雄

Chinese Hero

-Tales of the Blood Sword-

The classic martial arts epic,
illustrated by Wing Shing Ma,
brilliantly re-colored for
a new generation.

© Culturecom

DrM
PRODUCTION

Coming in March 2007.

PURI PURI

©Chiaki Taro

DrMaster
Publications Inc.
www.DrMasterbooks.com

SUGGESTED
AGES 15+

Wait, Don't Forget!

This book was printed in the original/Asian format. Please read panels from right to left.